The
Bougie ♡
Beaver

Best Selling Author
Bianca Bioni
Beaverly Hills, California

Hugs and Kisses!
I love you all!
xoxo,
Bianca

WANDA WEAVER

The. Bougie♡ Beaver

Written by
Bionca Bioni

Wanda Weaver,
The
Bougie
Beaver,
is quite the
well-kept overachiever!

She visits the spa
each and every week,
to avoid getting

TOO BUSHY

and

to stay

nice

and

sleek.

Most beavers are the less manicured kind, often

BUSHY

and unrefined.

They want to be just like her, *so refined* with well-manicured fur.

Wanda wears *fancy* clothes and *fancy* hats, And impresses even the *fanciest* pussy cats.

And in the evening,
she wears pearls

so

and

so

WHITE

that they

in the

full moonlight.

Wanda stays trim and fit playing lots of sports...

dressed in *Bougie* tops and expensive *designer* skorts.

Bougie
Beavers
love
playing
with balls...

they
love
them
rather
they are

BIG...
🏈🏈

or
rather
they
are
small.

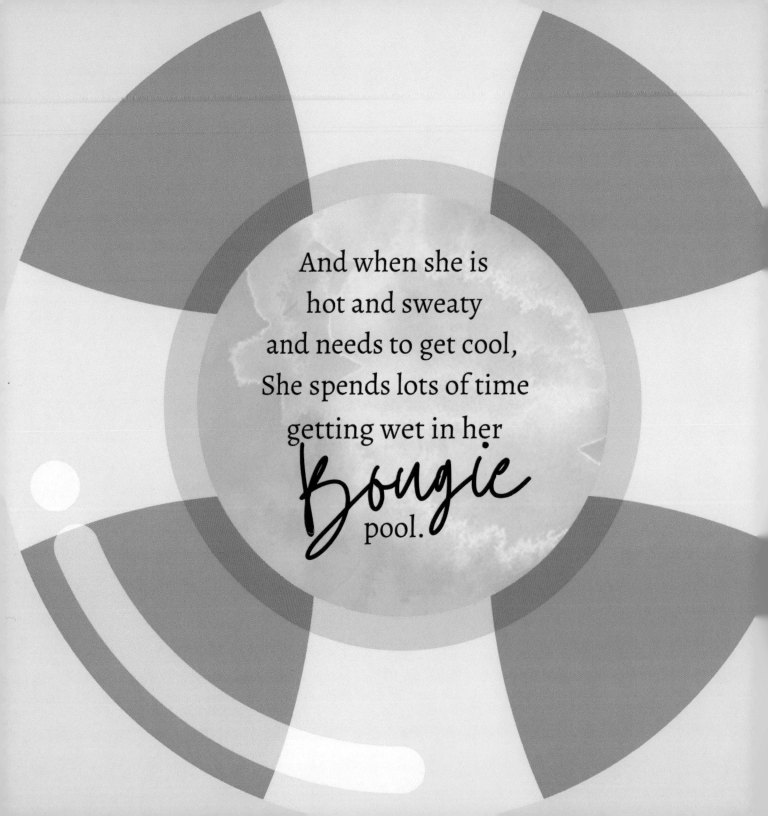

And when she is
hot and sweaty
and needs to get cool,
She spends lots of time
getting wet in her
Bougie
pool.

Wanda is such a kind beaver friend,
She lets all her friends come in.

"I have room for you all!
No matter if you are

BIG

and

THICK

or

THIN

and

small!"

Beavers may be
known for being

BUSHY

and

UNREFINED,

but...

Wanda Weaver,

The
Bougie
Beaver,

is the well-kept kind!

Every beaver wants
to be just like her...

fancy,

bougie,

and with

perfect fur.

About the Author

Bianca Bioni

Introducing the one and only bougie beaver of the literary world, the fabulous Bianca Bioni! Born in the exclusive enclave of Beaverly Hills, California, Bianca has clawed her way to the top of the best-seller lists, all while maintaining her impeccable fur coat and dazzling dental hygiene. And, of course, there's always a chilled flute of Beavergnac Prosecco nearby for those moments of sophisticated celebration.

From the moment she first nibbled on imported Swiss cheese, it was clear that Bianca was destined for greatness. Her lodge, more akin to a luxurious five-star spa, boasts amenities such as a beaver-sized jacuzzi, a built-in water feature showcasing her collection of designer dams, and a personal sushi chef to cater to her every aquatic craving— prosecco, of course, included.

Bianca's literary triumphs include titles like "Wanda Weaver: The Bougie Beaver," "Chic Chewing: A Beaver's Guide to Gourmet Wood," "Damsels and Dior: A Memoir of Time Spend Modeling for Damhouse Magazine," and "The Beaver's Guide to Luxury Log Cabin Living." When not busy writing her next bestseller, Bianca can be found reclining on her custom-made damask dam divan, enjoying a glass of rare bark-infused Bordeaux, or, when feeling extra fancy, a flute of Beavergnac Prosecco. She's also a tireless advocate for "Woodworker's Rights," a movement that champions the dignity and rights of the often-overlooked labor force behind the world's most luxurious wood-based products.

So, if you're in the mood for some hilarious tales of bougie beaver adventures, Bianca Bioni's books are sure to make a splash in your reading list.

Learn more about Bianca Bioni
and other fun Bougie Beaver gifts at
www.TheBougieBeaverandFriends.com

Wanda Weaver, The Bougie Beaver
Published by Golden Crown Publishing, LLC

www.GoldenCrownPublishing.com

Created by Bianca Bioni
ISBN:978-1-954648-84-5

Printed in Great Britain
by Amazon

41608917R00018